P9-DHS-585

I Can Read Fairy Tales

ILLUSTRATED BY
Gill Guile

BRIMAX

Contents

Goldilocks and the Three Bears

Once upon a time there was a Father Bear, a Mother Bear and a Baby Bear. They lived in a house in the middle of the forest. One day, Mother Bear made porridge for breakfast, but it was too hot to eat. "Let's go for a walk while the porridge cools," said Father Bear.

Goldilocks was walking in the forest too. She saw the Three Bears' house. The door was open, so she went inside. She tasted some porridge from the biggest bowl.
"That is too salty," said Goldilocks. She tasted some from the middle bowl.
"That is too sweet," said Goldilocks. She tasted some from the smallest bowl.
"That is just right," said Goldilocks, and she ate it all up.

Goldilocks saw three chairs. She sat on the biggest chair.
"That is too hard," said Goldilocks.
She sat on the middle chair.
"That is too soft," said Goldilocks.
She sat on the smallest chair.
"That is just right," said Goldilocks.
But Goldilocks wriggled so much that the little chair broke.

Then Goldilocks went upstairs.
She saw three beds. She laid on the biggest bed.
"That is too hard," said Goldilocks.
She laid on the middle bed.
"That is too soft," said Goldilocks.
She laid on the smallest bed.
"That is just right," said Goldilocks, and she fell fast asleep.

The Three Bears were very hungry when they came home.

"Who has been eating my porridge?" said Father Bear in his loud voice.

"Who has been eating my porridge?" said Mother Bear in her soft voice.

"Who has been eating my porridge?" said Baby Bear in his tiny voice. "It has all gone."

Father Bear sat down to think.
He jumped up!
"Who has been sitting in my chair?"
said Father Bear in his loud voice.
"Who has been sitting in my chair?"
said Mother Bear in her soft voice.
"Who has been sitting in my chair?"
said Baby Bear in his tiny voice.
"Look! It is broken."
The three bears went upstairs.

"Who has been sleeping in my bed?"
said Father Bear in his loud voice.
"Who has been sleeping in my bed?"
said Mother Bear in her soft voice.
"Who has been sleeping in my bed?"
said Baby Bear in his tiny voice.
"And look! She is still there!"
Goldilocks woke up and saw the
Three Bears. She ran downstairs and
out of the house, and was never seen
in the forest again.

Now the Three Bears always make sure that the door is locked when they go for a walk in the forest. They do not want anyone else eating their porridge, breaking their chairs or sleeping in their beds.

The Ugly Duckling

Mother Duck's eggs were hatching.
Soon she had five fluffy ducklings.
But one egg had not hatched.
"It is a goose egg," said the chicken.
"It is a turkey egg," said the goose.
"How will I know?" asked Mother
Duck.
"The baby will not swim," said the
goose. At last the egg hatched.
The funny, little duckling that came
out went for a swim straight away.

The other birds in the farmyard laughed at the ugly duckling. He was so unhappy he decided to run away. He came to a big lake and lived alone all summer. One day he saw some wild ducks.

"Will you be my friends?" he asked. But the wild ducks laughed at him. "What an ugly duckling you are!" they said.

When winter came, the ducks flew away. The ugly duckling stayed by the lake. One night it was so cold, the ugly duckling became trapped in the ice. The next morning a farmer set him free.

"Go and find your friends," said the farmer.

"I don't have any friends," said the ugly duckling.

When spring came, the wild ducks
returned to the lake. The ugly
duckling wanted to make friends
with them, but he was too scared.
"I wish they would speak to me," he
said. "I will look for a new home."
He flew up into the sky for the first
time. After a while he saw some
swans on a pond below him.
He flew down to speak to them.

"I am ugly and lonely," said the ugly duckling. "I do not want to live anymore."

"You are not ugly," said the swans. "Look at yourself in the pond. You are a swan."

The ugly duckling saw that he was a swan. He was so happy.

Two children came to the pond.

"A new swan!" they said. "Please stay with us."

The new swan knew he would never be lonely again.

Cinderella

Cinderella lived in a big house with her two ugly stepsisters. They made her do all the housework. The stepsisters spent a lot of time trying to make themselves look pretty. One day a letter arrived inviting them to a grand ball at the King's palace. "Can I come too?" asked Cinderella. "No - you must help us get ready," said the stepsisters.

Cinderella sat and watched as her
stepsisters left for the ball.
"If only I could go too," she said.
"You shall go to the ball," said
a voice.
Cinderella saw a lady in front of her.
"I am your fairy godmother," said
the lady.

"Bring me a pumpkin, four white mice and three green lizards," said the fairy godmother. With a wave of her wand she turned the pumpkin into a coach. The mice were turned into horses and the lizards became coachmen.

"What can I wear?" asked Cinderella.

The fairy godmother waved her wand again. Cinderella's rags became a pretty dress. On her feet were glass slippers.

"Now you can go to the ball," said the fairy godmother. "But remember - the magic ends at midnight." Cinderella arrived at the ball. No one knew who she was. The Prince danced with her all night. Cinderella was so happy, she forgot the time. Then the clock struck twelve.
"I must go!" said Cinderella to the Prince. She ran from the palace.

As Cinderella ran, one of her glass slippers fell off. Then the magic ended and the coach turned back into a pumpkin. The horses and coachmen turned back into mice and lizards. The Prince found Cinderella's glass slipper.
"I must find the girl who wears this slipper," he said. "She will be my bride."

The Prince took the slipper to every house in the kingdom. It fitted no one. At last he came to Cinderella's house. The first stepsister tried the slipper on. Her foot was too long. The second stepsister tried the slipper on. Her foot was too wide. When Cinderella tried the slipper, it fitted perfectly. The Prince married Cinderella, and they lived happily ever after.

The Three Little Pigs

The three little pigs lived with their mother. One day she said to them, "It is time you left home to build your own houses."

So the three little pigs walked to the crossroads. Then they each took different paths.

"Goodbye," they said to each other.

The first little pig built a house of straw. It was not very strong. One day he saw the big, bad wolf walking down the path. The wolf knocked on the door. He wanted to eat the little pig.

"Open the door, little pig, and let me come in." said the wolf.

"Not by the hair on my chinny chin chin will I open the door and let you come in," said the little pig.

"Then I will huff and puff and blow your house down," said the wolf. And he huffed and puffed until the house of straw was blown down. And that was the end of the first little pig.

The second little pig built a house of sticks. It was not very strong. One day he heard the big, bad wolf knocking at the door. He wanted the little pig for his dinner. The little pig was very scared.

"Open the door, little pig, and let me come in," said the wolf.

"Not by the hair on my chinny chin chin will I open the door and let you come in," said the little pig.

"Then I will huff and puff and blow your house down," said the wolf.

And he huffed and puffed until the house of sticks was blown down. And that was the end of the second little pig.

The third little pig built a house of bricks. It was very strong. One day he saw the big, bad wolf walking down the path. The little pig was not frightened.

"Open the door, little pig, and let me come in," he said.

"Not by the hair on my chinny chin chin will I open the door and let you come in," said the little pig.

"Then I will blow your house down," said the wolf. He huffed and puffed as hard as he could. But he couldn't blow down the house of bricks.

"I will go down the chimney," said the wolf. He climbed onto the roof.

The little pig heard the wolf on the roof. He put a big pot of water over the fire.

"The big, bad wolf will never catch me," said the little pig.

The wolf went down the chimney and fell SPLASH into the pot of hot water. And that was the end of him!

Little Red Riding Hood

Little Red Riding Hood's mother packed a basket with food. "Please take this basket to your Grandma," she said. "She isn't very well. Go straight to Grandma's house. Remember, do not talk to strangers on the way."

As Little Red Riding Hood walked through the forest, she stopped to pick some flowers for Grandma. "Good morning," said a voice behind her. "Where are you taking this basket of food?"

Little Red Riding Hood saw a big wolf. She forgot that she wasn't supposed to talk to strangers.

"I'm taking it to my Grandma," she said. "She lives in a house in the middle of the forest."

The wolf ran to Grandma's house.
He knocked on the door.
"Who's there?" called Grandma.
"It's Little Red Riding Hood," said the
wolf in a high voice.
"Come in," said Grandma.
When Grandma saw the wolf, she
jumped out of bed and locked
herself in a cupboard. Soon Little
Red Riding Hood knocked on the
door.
"Come in," said the wolf in
Grandma's voice.

Little Red Riding Hood went in and sat on Grandma's bed. As the wolf leaned forward, one of his ears popped out of the cap.
"Grandma, what big ears you have," said Little Red Riding Hood. "All the better to hear you with," said the wolf.

"Grandma, what big eyes you have," said Little Red Riding Hood, feeling a little bit frightened.
"All the better to see you with," said the wolf.
"Grandma, what big teeth you have," said Little Red Riding Hood.

"All the better to EAT you with!"
growled the wolf, and he jumped
out of bed.
"You're not my Grandma," cried
Little Red Riding Hood.
"No! I'm the big, bad wolf," growled
the wolf, and he chased her out of
the house.

"Help! Help" screamed Little Red Riding Hood.
A woodcutter heard her screams. When he saw the wolf, he chased him away. They went to Grandma's house to look for her.
"Grandma, it's me," called Little Red Riding Hood.

Only when Grandma was really sure did she open the cupboard door. Little Red Riding Hood hugged her and said, "I will never talk to strangers again. We were lucky that the big, bad wolf didn't hurt us."

Jack and the Beanstalk

Jack and his mother were very poor. One day Jack's mother sent him to market to sell their cow. On the way, Jack met a man.

"I will give you five magic beans for your cow," said the man.

Jack gave the cow to the man and took the beans home. His mother was very angry. She threw the beans out of the window and sent Jack to bed without any supper.

When Jack woke up the next morning, what a surprise he had! A huge beanstalk had grown overnight from the magic beans. Jack decided to climb up the beanstalk to see what he could find. When at last he reached the top, he walked along until he came to a big house.

The house belonged to a giant.
When Jack knocked on the door,
the giant's wife let him in and gave
him some breakfast. But then the
giant came home.
"Quick! Hide in the oven," said the
giant's wife.
"Fi fi fo fum!" roared the giant.
"I smell the blood of an Englishman!"
But the giant couldn't find Jack.

Then the giant called for his magic hen that laid golden eggs. Jack watched from the oven.
"Mother would like that hen," he said to himself. "Just think how rich we would be!"

After a while, the giant fell fast asleep. Jack took the hen and tucked it inside his shirt. Then he climbed back down the beanstalk and gave the hen to his mother. She was very pleased when she saw the golden eggs.

The next day, Jack climbed up the beanstalk again. He went to the giant's house and hid in a drawer.
"Fi fi fo fum!" roared the giant.
"I smell the blood of an Englishman!" But he couldn't find Jack anywhere.
The giant called for his magic harp. Jack listened as the harp played all by itself.
"Mother would like a harp like that," said Jack to himself.

When the giant fell asleep, Jack took the harp and hid it under his jacket. He began to run back to the beanstalk, but the harp began to play. The giant woke up and chased after Jack. Jack climbed back down the beanstalk as fast as he could. At the bottom, his mother handed him an axe.

Jack cut through the beanstalk with the axe. Both the giant and the beanstalk crashed to the ground and made a huge hole. The giant was never seen again. Jack and his mother were no longer poor. They lived happily ever after.